In space

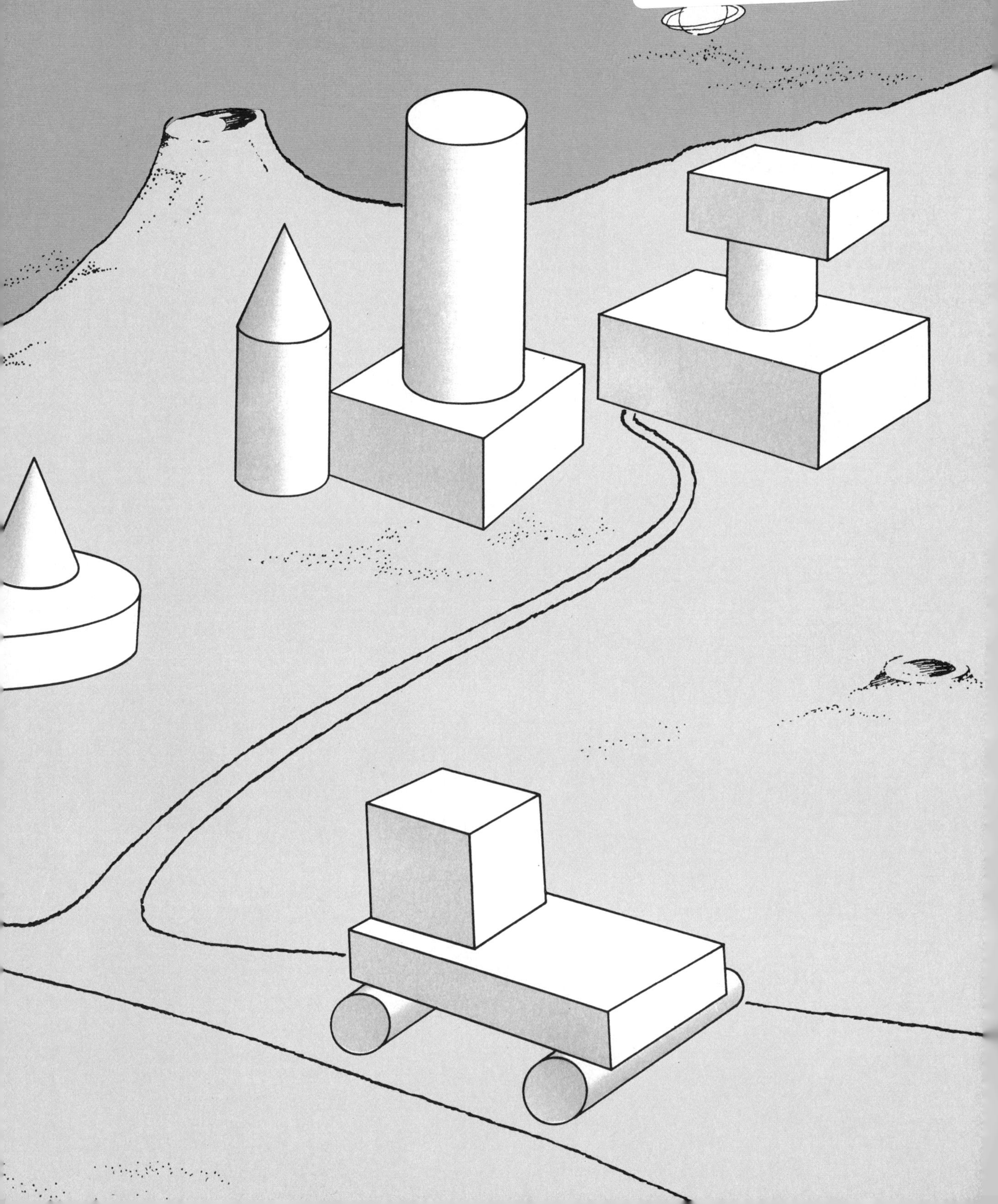

Match

Colour ![rectangular prism] How many? ☐

Colour ![cylinder] How many? ☐

Colour ![sphere] How many? ☐

In space

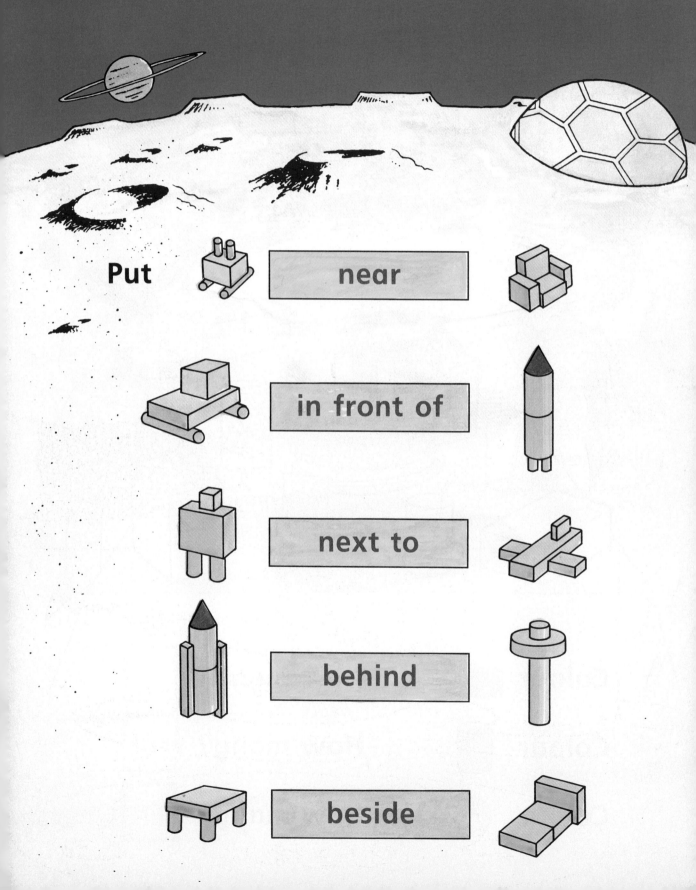

Put **near**

in front of

next to

behind

beside

Colour

the one above

the one at the bottom

the one inside

the one on top

A shape journey

Talk, make, tell a story.

Shape pictures

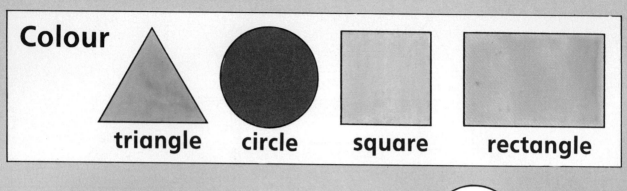

Colour

triangle   circle   square   rectangle

Match

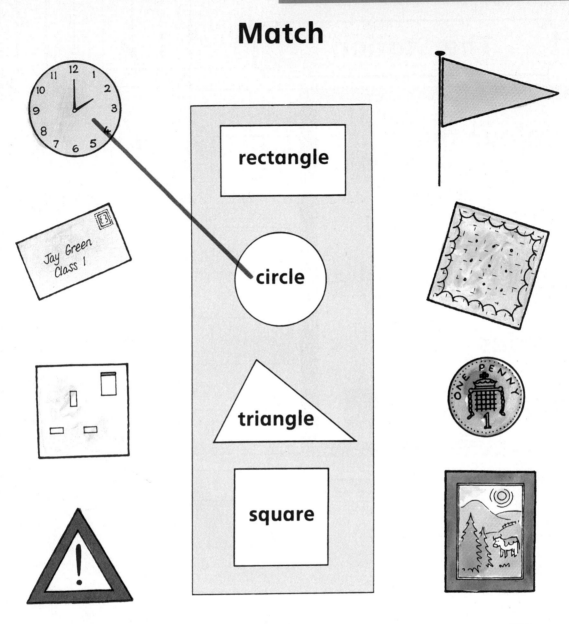

rectangle

circle

triangle

square

Draw

a sail

a square window

a round window

How many

squares

triangles

circles

rectangles?

Find the paths.

Colour triangles  .   Colour circles .

Fox

Badger

Who lives here?

Finish each pattern.

Cut and stick.

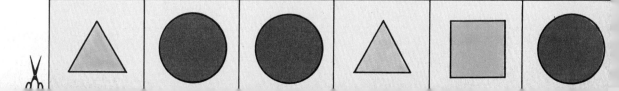

Ties

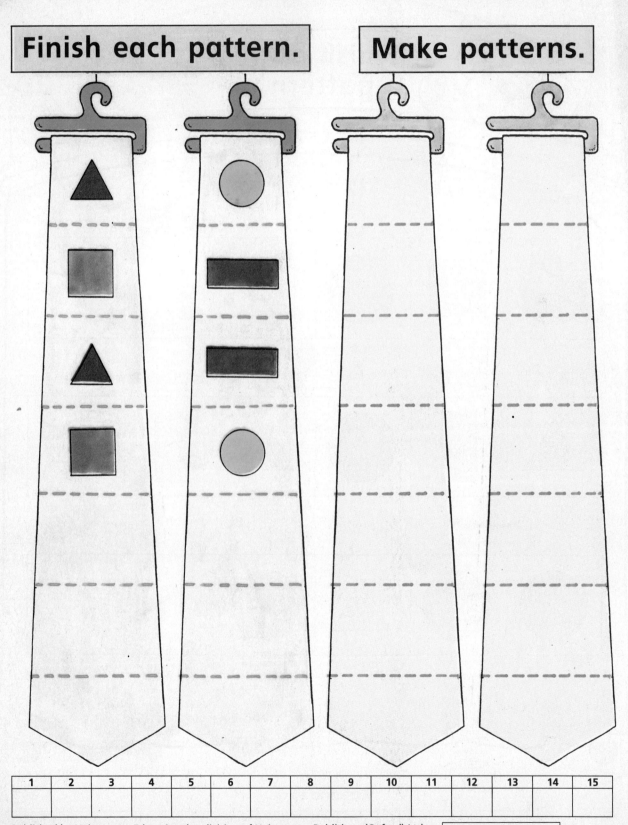

Finish each pattern.

Make patterns.

1	2	3	4	5	6	7	8	9	10	11	12	13	14	15

Published by Heinemann Educational, a division of Heinemann Publishers (Oxford) Ltd, Halley Court, Jordan Hill, Oxford OX2 8EJ. © Scottish Primary Mathematics Group 1991. ISBN 0 435 03709 9 Typeset and Illustrated by Oxprint Design. Printed by Jarrold Printing, Norwich.

95 96 97 98 99 10 9 8 7 6 5 4 3 2 1

ISBN 0-435-03090-6